Say the sounds and blend them together to read the word. Where is the frog in the picture?

frog

Say the word *tent* and listen out for the sounds: *tent* – /t-e-n-t/.
(There is one sound dot underneath the tent for each sound in the word.)

a big frog